This Book Belongs to:

....

A NEW BURLINGTON BOOK
The Old Brewery
6 Blundell Street
London N7 9BH

Consultant: Fiona Moss, RE Adviser at RE Today Services
Editor: Cathy Jones
Designer: Chris Fraser
Editorial Assistant: Tasha Percy
Design Manager: Anna Lubecka

First published in the United States by
Part of The Quarto Group
QEB Publishing
6 Orchard
Lake Forest, CA 92630

www.qed-publishing.co.uk

A CIP record for this book is available
from the Library of Congress.

ISBN 978 1 60992 569 7

Printed in China

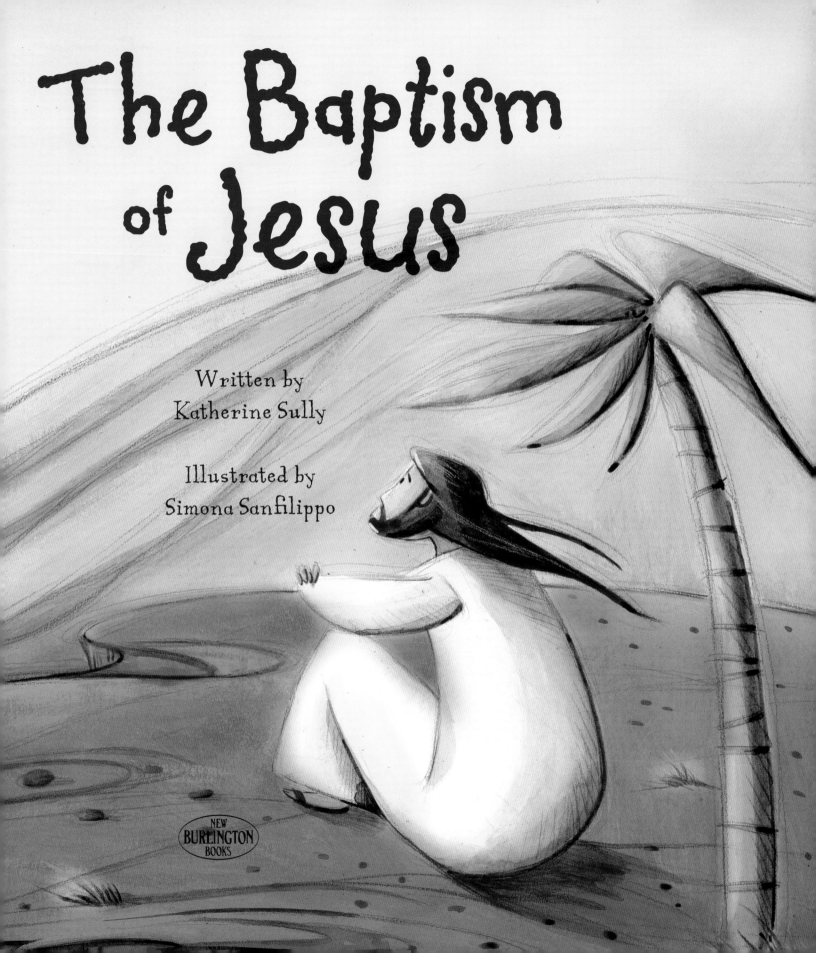

The Baptism of Jesus

Written by
Katherine Sully

Illustrated by
Simona Sanfilippo

NEW BURLINGTON BOOKS

Jesus had a cousin called John.
John traveled through the desert preaching.

He had no fine clothes
or food. His clothes were made
of camel hair tied around his
waist with a leather belt.

John told them, "Ask God to forgive all the bad choices you have made, live a better life, and it will lead to the kingdom of heaven."

"How do we do that?" asked the crowd.

"Come to the river today,
and I'll wash your sins away,"
said John.

Day after day, people came from far
and wide to the River Jordan.

One by one, John dipped
them in the river to
wash away their sins.

"I am baptizing you with water," he said,
"but someone else will come after me who will
baptize you with God's love."
The people wondered who he could mean.

Splash!

One day, Jesus came from Galilee to the River Jordan to be baptized.

"Why do you want me to baptize you?" asked John. "You should be baptizing me."

"I have come to the river today, because this is the right way," said Jesus.

So John baptized Jesus in the River Jordan.

As soon as Jesus was baptized, heaven opened,
and God's love came down like a dove.

A voice from heaven said,
"This is my Son, whom I love."

Could this man, Jesus, be the Son of God,
the people wondered.

After he was baptized, Jesus went into the desert.
For forty days and forty nights, he was
alone in the desert.

The hot sun beat
down and the desert
wind blew.

He had plenty of time
to think, but Jesus
had nothing to eat.
He was very hungry.

Then, the devil came to test Jesus with bad thoughts.

He whispered in Jesus' ear,
"If you are the Son of God, tell
these stones to become bread."

But Jesus replied,
"We can't live just on bread.
We need God's love, too."

The devil took Jesus
to a high tower.

Then the devil whispered a second time.
"If you are the Son of God," he said,
"throw yourself off this tower.
God's angels will catch you."

But Jesus replied, "If we have trust in God,
we don't need to test him."

The devil took Jesus to a mountaintop.
For a third time, the devil whispered,
"If you worship me, I will give you
all the kingdoms of the world."

But Jesus replied, "No, go away!
We should only worship God."

Jesus pushed the devil away.
Then angels came and looked after him.

When Jesus came back from the desert, he received bad news. His cousin, John, had spoken out against the king and had been put in prison.

Cluck!

Cheep!

Cluck!

Jesus remembered what John had said.

Cheep!

From that time on, Jesus told everyone he met, "Ask God to forgive all the bad choices you have made, live a better life, and it will lead to the kingdom of heaven."

Next Steps

Look back through the book to find more to talk about and join in with.

* Copy the actions. Do the actions with the characters—pretend to sprinkle water on someone's head; pretend to flap your wings like a dove; whisper in someone's ear.

* Join in with the rhyme. Pause to encourage joining in with "Come to the river today, and I'll wash your sins away."

* Count in threes or fours. Count the sheep, the hens, the children.

* Name the colors. What colors can you find in the crowd?

* All shapes and sizes. Look for big, middle-size, and small sheep and hens.

* Listen to the noises in the story. When you see the word on the page, point and make the sound—Splash! Baa! Bzzzzz!

Now that you've read the story . . . what do you remember?

* Who was John?
* Why was he called John the Baptist?
* Where was Jesus baptized?
* What happened when Jesus was baptized?
* Who tempted Jesus, and how many times was he tempted?
* What did Jesus tell people that John the Baptist had told him?

What does the story tell us?
Jesus was chosen by God, and his trust in God was tested.